WISCONSIN BADGERS FACTS & TRIVIA

BY

Jeff & Linda Everson

The E. B. Houchin Company

1994

Wautoma, Wisconsin

The E. B. Houchin Company
P.O. Box 673
Wautoma, Wisconsin 54982

ISBN: 0-938313-07-X

First Printing: September 1994

TABLE OF CONTENTS

FACTS

1
A SPORTS TRADITION

The University of Wisconsin's sports program is steeped in tradition. Dating back to the late 1800s, Wisconsin has excelled and supported sports as an alternative to the special education students receive at Madison. Not only in Madison, but all other Universities included in the Wisconsin school system have followed suit with sports and education.

Possibly because of the level of education expected at Wisconsin, sports have not been as competative with the opponents through the years. Wisconsin has struggled through many years of fair to mediocre finishes. Only until recently has Wisconsin sports erupted from these stagnate years.

When one looks back at the history of Badger sports, you cannot forget the 29 and 23 game winning streaks of the basketball teams of the mid-to-late 1910s. The winning of the NCAA basketball tournament in 1941. The four Rose Bowl appearances of the Wisconsin football teams and the continued success of the hockey program since the sport was brought back as a major sport in 1963, cumulating with five NCAA championships.

Wisconsin is coming off one of the most (if not the most) successful men's sports seasons in the history of the school. Beginning with the football team's first victory in the infamous Rose Bowl game. Continuing with the first bid to the NCAA tournament for the basketball team since the 1947 season and finally the Badger hockey team falling just short of another Final Four finish in the 1994 NCAA tournament.

It is not possible to say enough about the hockey program. As the other major sports floundered, the hockey program has flourished at Wisconsin, not having a losing season since 1976. While attendance at the other sports at Wisconsin has rode a roller coaster ride, the hockey fans in Madison have led the nation since the 1970 season. Now it seems as if the fans of Wisconsin are back at Camp Randall for the football team and back at the fieldhouse for the basketball team. Now they can join the nation's number one fans at the Dane County Coliseum for hockey as the number one college sports fans in America.

Hopefully this trivia book can spark some memories. Enjoy the book. Go Badgers!

Jeff & Linda Everson

P.S. We apologize for the lack of Facts & Trivia for any of the Women's sports. When we made inquiries with the university athletic and public relations departments, we were told that none were available. We hope to remedy this oversight in future editions of this work.

2
FOOTBALL CAREER LEADERS

RUSHING YARDS
Billy Marek　3,709

PASSING YARDS
Randy Wright　5,003

RECEPTIONS
Al Toon　131

FIELD GOALS MADE
Todd Gregorie　65

EXTRA POINTS MADE
Vince Lamia　105

PUNTS ATTEMPTED
Scott Cepicky　249

PUNT RETURNS
Thad McFadden　75

PUNT RETURN TOUCHDOWNS
Ira Matthews　4

KICKOFF RETURNS
Fred Owens　84

KICKOFF RETURN TOUCHDOWNS
Danny Crooks and Ira Matthews　2

INTERCEPTONS
Neovia Greyer   18

INTERCEPTIONS FOR TDS
Bob Radcliffe   3

SOLO TACKLES
Tim Krumrie   276

ASSISTED TACKLES
Dave Crossen   205

TOTAL TACKLES
Gary Casper   447

PASSES DEFENDED
Troy Vincent   31

FUMBLES RECOVERED
Dan Batsch   7

BLOCKED KICKS
Richard Johnson   8

3
BASKETBALL CAREER LEADERS

GAMES PLAYED
Tim Locum   118
Kurt Portmann   118
Danny Jones   118

GAMES STARTED
Rick Olson   112

MINUTES PLAYED
Rick Olson   3,962

POINTS
Danny Jones   1,854

SCORING AVERAGE
Clarence Sherrod   19.6

FIELD GOALS
Rick Olson   729

FIELD GOAL ATTEMPTS
Rick Olson   1,535

FIELD GOAL PERCENTAGE
Patrick Tompkins   .573

3-POINT FIELD GOALS
Tim Locum   227

3-POINT FG ATTEMPTS
Tim Locum   481

3-POINT FG PERCENTAGE
Mike Heinman   .475

FREE THROWS
Claude Gregory   433

FREE THROW ATTEMPTS
Danny Jones   599

FREE THROW PERCENTAGE
Rick Olson   .870

REBOUNDS
Claude Gregory   904

REBOUNDING AVERAGE
Joe Franklin   11.9

ASSISTS
Tracy Webster   501

BLOCKED SHOTS
Brad Sellers   120

STEALS
Tracy Webster   183

4
HOCKEY CAREER LEADERS

POINTS SCORED
Mike Eaves   267

GOALS SCORED
Mark Johnson   125

ASSISTS
Theran Welsh   104

PENALTY MINUTES
Bob Suter   377

HAT TRICKS
Bert DeHate   15

GAMES PLAYED
Rob Andringa   179

SAVES BY GOALTENDERS
Duane Derksen   3,222

VICTORIES BY GOALIES
Duane Derksen   80

SHUTOUTS BY GOALIES
Terry Kleisinger   9

LOWEST GOAL-AGAINST AVE.
Curtis Joseph   2.49

SAVE PERCENTAGE
Curtis Joseph   .922

WON-LOSS PERCENTAGE
Marc Behrend   .842

5
WISCONSIN BADGERS CHRONOLOGY

1889 - First Wisconsin football game played against Calumet Club. Lost 27-0.

1900 - Wisconsin wins first basketball game against Wayland Academy.

1901 - Badgers first undefeated football season and run a winning streak of 17 straight games.

1912 - Badgers win their first solo Big Ten championship in basketball.

1911-13 - Wisconsin wins 29 consectutive basketball games.

1913-15 - Badgers win 23 straight basketball games.

1917 - Camp Randall Stadium is built for football.

1930 - Wisconsin Field House is new home for the basketball team.

1934 - Wisconsin discontinues hockey as a sport.

1941 - Badgers win the NCAA basketball tournament.

1953 - Wisconsin plays in their first Rose Bowl game against USC.

1960 - Wisconsin plays in their second Rose Bowl game against Washington.

1962 - Hockey is brought back as a sport at Wisconsin.

1963 - Badgers play in their third Rose Bowl game against USC.
  - Wisconsin wins first hockey game in 28 years.

1967-69 - Badgers go winless in 23 straight football games.

1970 - Wisconsin plays in their first NCAA Hockey tournament. Places third place.

1973 - Badgers win their first NCAA Hockey tournament.

1977 - Badgers win second NCAA Hockey tournament.

1981 - Wisconsin wins third NCAA Hockey tournament.
  - Wisconsin plays in the Garden State Bowl against Tennessee.

1982 - Wisconsin plays against Kansas State in the Indepencence Bowl. Records first Bowl win.

1983 - Wisconsin wins fourth NCAA Hockey tournament.

1984 - Wisconsin plays in the Hall of Fame Bowl against Kentucky.

1989 - Badgers play in the NIT basketball tournament. First tournament bid since 1947.

1990 - Wisconsin wins fifth NCAA Hockey championship.

1994 - Wisconsin plays in their fourth Rose Bowl Game. First Rose Bowl victory against UCLA.
  - Badgers receive first NCAA basketball tournament bid since 1947.

QUESTIONS

WISCONSIN BADGERS BASKETBALL

1
INDIVIDUAL RECORDS

1. This Badger averaged 15.3 points a game in his junior year, but he exploded for 42 points against Indiana on March 8, 1965. This mark still stands as the most points scored in a game by a Badger. Who is he?

2. What Badger is the all-time leading scorer in points scored?

3. Who made 14 of 14 free throws against Purdue on February 13, 1986?

4. He led the Badgers four straight seasons in blocked shots from 1978 through 1982. He also leads Wisconsin in total overall rebounds and was drafted by the Washington Bullets. Who is he?

5. This Milwaukee Lincoln High School star tops the Badgers in career scoring average and is fifth in overall points scored. He also made the Academic All-Big Ten in 1970. Who is he?

6. Who led Wisconsin with 23 points against Rice in the NIT tournament loss on March 17, 1993?

7. Wes Matthews made how many straight free throws between December 1979 and January 1980?

8. This Badger leads Wisconsin with a career high 120 blocked shots in two seasons as a freshman and sophomore, but transferred to Ohio State to finish his collegiate career. Who is he?

9. What Badger led the team with 344 rebounds (most ever in one season for Wisconsin) in 1951?

10. Only three Badgers in their Wisconsin careers averaged over 10 rebounds a game. Can you name two of them?

11. Which Badger led the team in assists, steals, 3-point percentage, 3-pointers made, games started and games played in the 1992-93 season?

12. What Purdue star scored 50 points against Wisconsin at the Fieldhouse on January 27, 1962 and later played for Chicago, Baltimore and the Detroit Pistons in the NBA?

13. He made 13 of 14 field goal attempts against Wisconsin on December 20, 1975 in Madison. He was drafted by the Milwaukee Bucks and coached the Dallas Mavericks in the NBA. Who is he?

14. This Shawano High School star scored 27 points for the Badgers in the second half against Loyola (IL) on December 12, 1959. No Badger has equalled this mark. Who is he?

15. Who was the All-American center on the UCLA team that beat Wisconsin, 100-56, on December 28, 1966?

16. Who was the only Badger named as the team's most improved player two consecutive years?

17. Who was the only Badger to be named captain for three separate years? What years?

18. He averaged only 14 points a game in 1990-91, but he made almost 64% of his shots that season to set a Badger record. Who is he?

19. Who is the only Wisconsin player to make over 90% of his free throws in a season? What season?

20. This Badger grabbed 30 rebounds against Purdue, January 3, 1953, setting a Wisconsin record. Who is he?

21. Only three Badgers have made more than 400 free throws in a season. Can you name two of them?

22. Three Badgers have started over 100 games for Wisconsin. Can you name two?

23. Twice he made seven 3-point field goals in a game and twice he made six 3-point field goals in a game for Wisconsin. Who is he?

24. These two Badgers scored a combined 1,185 points in the 1988-89 season and helped Wisconsin to their first ever NIT tournament bid. Who were these two Badgers?

25. He is the only Wisconsin player to score over 1,000 total points in his first two seasons. Who is he?

26. Who was the last Badger to score 30 points in consecutive games prior to the 1993-94 season?

2
TEAM RECORDS

1. Prior to the 1993-94 season, what was the last year the Badgers played in the NCAA tournament?

2. In what year was the first Wisconsin game played at the Fieldhouse?

3. What team has the longest running Big Ten rivalry against Wisconsin? What year did the two teams first play?

4. The Badgers have beaten what Big Ten team the most times?

5. Wisconsin scored 120 points to set a school scoring record that still stands today. The game was played on December 9, 1967. Who was the opponent?

6. What year did the Badgers first score 100 points in a game? Against what team?

7. What team did Wisconsin beat to win the NCAA tournament in 1941?

8. What did the headline read in the *Wisconsin State Journal* after the Badgers won the NCAA tournament in 1941?

9. In the 1965-66 season all five Badger starters averaged over 10 points a game. Can you name three of them?

10. What was the last season the Badgers won the Big Ten conference and were invited to the NCAA tournament prior to the 1993-94 season?

11. What was the last year Wisconsin beat Indiana in basketball?

12. How many overtimes did Wisconsin play against Indiana in a 1987 game before losing, 86-85?

13. Including the 1993-94 season the Badgers have played Bobby Knight's Indiana Hoosiers 44 times. How many games has Wisconsin won?

14. Can you name the University that Wisconsin beat by 55 points on December 14, 1988?

15. On March 7, 1913 what team stopped a 29-game winning streak for Wisconsin that covered two seasons? The Badgers lost by how many points?

16. How many straight games did Wisconsin win after the 29-game winning streak was broken?

17. How many times were the Badgers the Big Ten champions or co-champions?

18. Sporting an 11-0 record and ranked 12th nationally the Badgers were beaten 90-53 by what Big Ten team on January 12, 1994?

19. On March 3, 1962 the Badgers defeated the number one nationally ranked Ohio State Buckeyes, 86-67. Can you name three of the five starters on the Buckeyes?

20. Wisconsin played in 15 Milwaukee Classic tournaments between 1962-76. How many Classics did the Badgers win? What years?

21. Marquette University won the NCAA tournament in 1977. The Badgers played Marquette twice during the season. Did Wisconsin win either game? Who was the Badgers coach that season? Who coached Marquette that season?

22. How many years has it been since Wisconsin was ranked in the national top 20 schools prior to the 1993-94 season?

23. In the 1946-47 and the 1958-59 seasons the Badgers defeated only one Big Ten opponent each year. What team did the Badgers beat in the 1946-47 season? What team did the Badgers defeat in the 1958-59 season?

24. After starting the 1975-76 season with eight wins in 10 games, the Badgers lost how many games in a row?

25. What team was the opponent the night Wisconsin made all 22 free throw attempts?

26. The Badgers set a team record attempting 61 free throws against Michigan on February 21, 1953. How many free throws did Wisconsin make? Did the Badgers win?

27. Wisconsin became a charter member of the Big Ten conference in what year?

28. Wisconsin had played this opponent five times in their basketball history, but has been handed two of the biggest losses ever. What team was Wisconsin's opponent?

29. The 1989 Badgers won one and lost one in the NIT tournament marking the first post season play for Wisconsin basketball in 41 years. What team did Wisconsin beat? What opponent did the Badgers lose to?

30. What team was Wisconsin's first opponent in the 1994 NCAA tournament? Did the Badgers win?

3
PERSONALITIES

1. What were the names of the 6'11" twins that played for the Badgers during the 1972-74 seasons?

2. What former Wisconsin basketball head coach is currently color commentator for local television broadcasts?

3. This Badger was named to Team USA in 1993. Who is he?

4. Who was the only Badger named team MVP three years in a row?

5. What Beloit Memorial High School standout, who won the 1970 WIAA High School tournament with a last second half court shot to beat Neenah, was the number one substitiute for Wisconsin in 1973-74?

6. This player was named "Mr. Basketball" in Illinois playing for Martin Luther King High School in Chicago. He is also the heaviest Badger to put on a basketball uniform. Who is he?

7. Can you name two of the three 7'0" Badgers?

8. His father played on the Milwaukee Brewers from 1978-81. Who is he and what years did he play for Wisconsin?

9. Who was the last Badger named to the All-American first team and what season was he picked?

10. This Badger's father was a very successful high school coach at Whitefish Bay. Who is he?

11. Who was the Badgers Rose Bowl quarterback in 1960 and also lettered in basketball in 1959?

12. What is the name of the Wisconsin Athletic Director hired in 1992 that lettered in football and basketball?

4
NATIONAL BASKETBALL ASSOCIATION

1. Through the years the Milwaukee Bucks have drafted three Badgers. Can you name two of them?

2. Two Badgers were drafted in the first round of the NBA draft. Who were they?

3. Stu Jackson was the head coach of what NBA team before taking the Wisconsin head coaching basketball job?

4. What Badger was also a star for the old Oshkosh All-Stars of the NBA?

5
COACHES

1. What successful UW-Eau Claire head basketball coach accepted the Badger coaching job, only to turn it down later?

2. Who coached the Badgers to their only undefeated seasons? What seasons?

3. Who coached Wisconsin to their only NCAA Championship in 1941?

4. What Badger head coach became the first general manager of the Milwaukee Bucks?

5. This Wisconsin head coach won only 28% against the Big Ten conference from 1983-92. Who is he?

6. What successful Badger football coach was an assistant coach for Wisconsin basketball in the 1968-69 season?

7. Who was the Badgers head coach that took Wisconsin to the NCAA tournaments in 1941 and 1947?

8. Who coached the Badgers to their 29-game winning streak?

9. Who was the head coach of Wisconsin's first 20-game losing record? What year?

10. Prior to the 1993-94 season, Wisconsin had only one 20-game winning season. What year and who was the head coach?

11. Who coached Wisconsin in the first six seasons of basketball from 1899-1904?

6
FIRSTS

1. Who was the first Badger to be named Big Ten Most Valuable Player? In what year?

2. Who was the first Badger with over 100 assists in a season? What year?

3. Who was Wisconsin's first 1,000 point man?

4. Who was the first Badger to make over 200 field goals in a season?

5. What was the Big Ten conference first named?

6. Who was the first Badger to make over 300 free throws in his Wisconsin career?

7
WHAT NUMBER DID THEY WEAR?

1. Claude Gregory?
2. Tracy Webster?
3. Rick Olson?
4. Willie Simms?
5. Trent Jackson?
6. Brad Sellers?
7. Ken Siebel?
8. Ken Barnes?
9. Dale Koehler?
10. Michael Finley?
11. Danny Jones?
12. Joe Franklin?
13. Wes Matthews?
14. Don Rehfeldt?
15. Kim Hughes?

8
WHAT POSITION DID THEY PLAY?

1. Chuck Nagle?
2. Mike O'Melia?
3. Albert Nicholas?
4. Wes Matthews?
5. J.J. Weber?
6. Cory Blackwell?
7. Tom Hughbanks?
8. Don Rehfeldt?
9. Ken Gustafson?
10. Clarence Sharrod?
11. Larry Petty?
12. Rod Ripley?
13. Trent Jackson?
14. Tracy Webster?
15. Robert Cook?
16. Jack Brens?

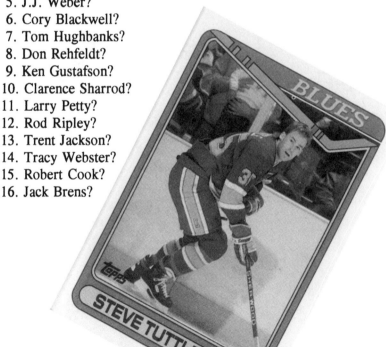

QUESTIONS

WISCONSIN BADGERS FOOTBALL

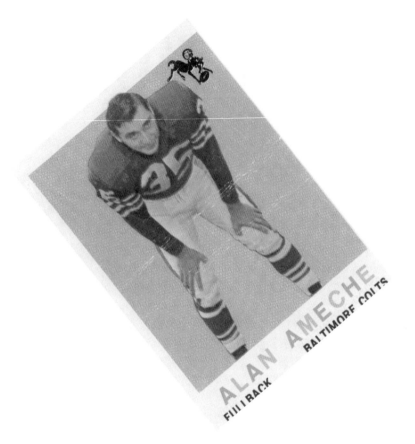

1
TEAM RECORDS

1. Wisconsin was one of the charter members of the Intercollegiate Conference of Faculty Represenatives. In what year was the conference begun?

2. What year did the Badgers play their first football games?

3. What team has the longest running rivalry in football with Wisconsin? What year did the two teams first play each other?

4. The Badgers won their third conference title in six years and this is the first undefeated team (9-0) in Wisconsin history. What year was this?

5. In 1993 the Badgers won a slice of national respect with what record?

6. In the fifth game of the 1993 season against Northwestern, the Badgers set a new rushing touchdown record. How many touchdowns did Wisconsin score? Who scored the touchdowns?

7. When was the last time the Badgers had a punt snap go through the end zone and what team was it done against?

8. When was the last time Wisconsin returned a kickoff for a touchdown? Against what opponent?

9. When was the last time an opponent returned a kickoff for a touchdown against the Badgers and what team accomplished this?

10. When was the last time the Badgers returned an interception for a touchdown? Against what team?

11. When was the last time an opponent intercepted a Badgers' pass and returned it for a touchdown? What team was this?

12. The Badgers have been ranked as the nation's number one team only once in school history. What date was this?

13. Wisconsin has upset the nation's number one ranked team three times. What teams were ranked number one when the Badgers defeated them? What seasons did this happen?

14. What is the Wisconsin team record for the most touchdowns during a game? Against what team?

15. What is the Badgers team record for the most field goals in a game. Against what three opponents has this happened?

16. What is the Wisconsin team record for the number of punts in a game? Against what team and what season?

17. What is the longest Wisconsin winning streak? What seasons?

18. What is the record for the longest Badger home winning streak? What seasons?

19. Wisconsin won nine games in a season five times. Can you name the years this occurred?

20. Wisconsin has had three undefeated teams. What years did this happen? What were the Badgers' records?

21. How many Big Ten Conference championships have the Badgers won? What seasons?

22. What other Wisconsin university did the Badgers defeat 106-0? What season?

23. What three seasons did the Badgers go winless?

24. Since 1896 Wisconsin has won the Big Ten title nine times. Can you name four of the nine years?

25. Since 1940 season, Wisconsin has had how many winless seasons in the Big Ten? What years?

26. What is the Badgers homecoming record?

2
CAMP RANDALL STADIUM

1. Camp Randall Stadium is among the nation's largest college owned stadiums. Rounding off to the nearest 1,000, what is the seating capacity?

2. When was the first game played at Camp Randall?

3. This first game at Camp Randall Stadium was a thrilling homecoming victory over which archrival?

4. The University of Wisconsin band is recognized for their post game celebration which is known as what?

5. Who is the current (1994) director of the University of Wisconsin band?

6. What Badger scored 30 points in 1974 to set a Camp Randall Stadium record that still stands?

7. To open the 1993 campaign Wisconsin drew their largest opening day home crowd in eight years. Can you recall the attendance within 1,000?

8. Who holds the Camp Randall Stadium record for the longest punt return? How long was the return?

9. Who kicked the longest field goal at Camp Randall Stadium? How long was the kick?

10. What Badger has the Camp Randall Stadium record for the longest pass interception return. How long was the return?

11. What was the distance of the longest run from scrimmage at Camp Randall Stadium? Who holds this record?

12. Two Badgers have the record for the longest kickoff return at Camp Randall Stadium. Who are they? How long was the return?

13. Who holds the record for the longest pass reception at Camp Randall Stadium? How long was the pass and who threw it?

3
PERSONALITIES

1. In 1954 this Badger became the only Wisconsin player to win the Heisman Trophy. Who is he?

2. In 1990 which Badger became the first four-time first team Academic All-American in NCAA history?

3. What former Wisconsin quarterback is currently the color commentator of the Badger radio broadcasts?

4. The University of Wisconsin has retired four numbers in its football history. Can you name three of the four stars and what were the numbers they wore?

5. Since 1980 there have been three players picked in the top 10 overall National Football League draft. Can you name them?

6. On opening day 1992, there were 11 Badgers on NFL rosters. Name five of them?

7. Seven Wisconsin football players have been elected to the College Football Hall of Fame since it's establishment in 1955. Can you name three of the seven?

8. What Wisconsin Badger was named Big Ten most valuable player in 1949 and also received the Chicago *Tribune*'s Silver Trophy?

9. What Badger was drafted by the NFL in 1993? What NFL team drafted him?

10. Who is the only Badger football player to be selected to the

Academic All-American team four times?

11. What Wisconsin defensive back played in the 1991 East-West Shrine Game?

12. In 1992 two Badgers participated in the Japan Bowl in Tokyo, Japan. Who are they?

13. What Badger and former Green Bay Packer played in the 1963 East-West Shrine Game and the 1964 Hula Bowl?

14. Two Badgers were listed in the top 10 voting for the Heisman Trophy in 1962. Can you name them?

15. Three Badgers were drafted in the first round of the NFL draft in 1985. Can you name them?

16. What Badger was the last nine-time letter winner in Wisconsin's history?

17. What is the full name of Wisconsin's mascot?

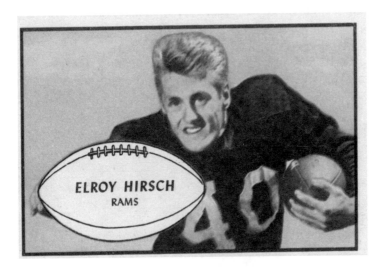

ELROY HIRSCH
RAMS

4
INDIVIDUAL RECORDS

1. There have been five backs in Wisconsin history that have gained 1,000 yards rushing in a season. Who are they?

2. Who holds the Wisconsin record for the best punting average in a game? What was his average length of punts?

3. Who holds the Badger record for the most punt return yardage in a game?

4. Who holds the Wisconsin record for the most punt returns in a game?

5. This Badger holds the record for the longest reception in school's history. Who is he?

6. Who holds the Wisconsin record for the longest punt? How long was it?

7. Two Wisconsin quarterbacks are tied for the most touchdown passes in a season. Who are they? How many touchdowns did they throw for?

8. What is the Wisconsin record for interceptions in a game? Who holds the record?

9. Who holds the Badger record for solo tackles in a game? How many tackles?

10. One Badger returned two interceptions for touchdowns in a game. Who is he? Against what opponent?

11. What Wisconsin player holds the record for fumbles recovered in a game?

12. This Badger blocked three punts in a game. Who is he? What date did this happen?

13. What Badger holds the season record for field goals made? How many?

14. This Badger returned three punts for touchdowns in a season. Who is he?

15. Who holds the Badger season record for blocked kicks? What season?

16. This Wisconsin quarterback has the season record for pass attempts. Who is he? How many?

17. What Badger quarterback has the season record for pass completions? How many?

18. Who holds the Wisconsin season record for receiving yards? How many?

19. Two Wisconsin receivers are tied for the receptions record in a season. Who are they? How many passes did they catch?

20. What Badger holds the season record for pass receiving touchdowns? How many?

21. What Badger has the season record for rushing touchdowns? How many touchdowns?

22. Who holds the season record for rushing attempts for Wisconsin? How many?

23. What kicker has the Badger season record for 45 extra points made?

24. Who has the Wisconsin record in a season for punts attempted? How many?

25. This Badger had 32 punt returns to set a season record. Who is he?

26. What Badger has had more kickoff returns in a season that any other? How many?

27. Who holds the Wisconsin season record for kickoff return yardage? How many yards?

28. One Badger intercepted nine passes in a season setting a school record. Who is he?

29. Who holds the Badger season record for interception return yardage? How many yards?

30. This Badger had 102 solo tackles in a season setting a Wisconsin record. Who is he?

31. What Wisconsin player had the season record for total tackles? How many?

32. Two Wisconsin players hold the season record for tackles made for losses. Who are they? How many tackles did they make?

33. What Badger holds the season record for tackles for loss yardage? How many yards?

34. Two Badgers rank fourth on the Big Ten single season rushing tandems list. Who are they? What is their total yards?

5
THE 1993 SEASON

1. In the 1993 opener against Nevada, the Wisconsin quarterback Darrell Bevell set a new record. What was the record?

2. Bevell set a school record for passing yardage in the 1993 game against Minnesota. How many yards did he pass for? How many completions?

3. Bevell broke the Badgers' season completion record that was set in 1950. Whose record did Bevell break?

4. A Wisconsin defensive tackle led the Big Ten in the 1993 season with 10 sacks. Who is he?

5. What Badger cornerback led the Big Ten with six interceptions and finished seventh nationally?

6. What Wisconsin linebacker was credited with a league leading five forced fumbles in 1993?

7. What Badger rushed for 100 yards or more in 10 of Wisconsin's regular season games?

8. In the 1993 season the Badgers had a huge victory on October 30. What Big Ten team did the Badgers defeat? What was the score?

9. What was the only team to defeat the 1993 Badgers? What was the score?

10. Who was the "walk-on" kicker for the 1993 Badgers?

11. The Badgers played in the Coca-Cola Bowl. What was the date? Where was the game played? Against what team?

12. What was Wisconsin ranked in the national polls at the end of the 1993 regular season?

13. Who had the most rushing yards in a season, breaking the record during the 1993 year? How many yards?

6
COACHES

1. Who was the Badgers first football head coach?

2. Who holds the longest term of head coach in Wisconsin's history of football?

3. Who was the head coach when Wisconsin won the Big Ten title in 1952 and made its first appearance in the Rose Bowl?

4. Who was the only head coach in Wisconsin's history to take the Badgers to two Rose Bowls and three finishes in the nation's Top Ten rankings?

5. The 1984 Badger football team was one of the most talented in the school's history. Who was the head coach of the team that season? How many players were drafted in the 1985 NFL draft?

6. What head coach has the best winning percentage in the school's history?

7
THE LESSER BOWLS

1. What team defeated the Badgers in the 1981 Garden State Bowl? What was the score?

2. What team did the Badgers defeat in the 1982 Independence Bowl? What was the score?

3. What team defeated the Badgers in the 1984 Hall of Fame Bowl? What was the score?

4. In the 1981 Garden State Bowl, who was the Badgers leading rusher? How many yards?

5. In the 1981 Garden State Bowl, who was Wisconsin's leading passer? How many yards did he throw for?

6. Who was the Badgers leading receiver in the Garden State Bowl? How many receptions? How many yards?

7. Within 1,000, how many people attended the 1981 Garden State Bowl?

8. Who was the Badgers leading rusher in the 1982 Independence Bowl? How many yards?

9. What was the name of Wisconsin's passing leader in the 1982 Independence Bowl? How many yards?

10. Who was Wisconsin's leading receiver in the 1982 Independence Bowl? How many catches? How many yards?

11. Who was the game's offensive most valuable player of the

1982 Independence Bowl? Who was the game's defensive most valuable player?

12. What future Green Bay Packer quarterback played in the 1982 Independence Bowl?

13. What weather condition held the anticipated crowd of 49,000 down to 24,684 for the 1982 Independence Bowl?

14. What was the deciding play in the Wisconsin's loss in the 1984 Hall of Fame Bowl?

15. Who was the leading rusher in the 1984 Hall of Fame Bowl for Wisconsin? How many yards?

16. Who led Wisconsin in passing in the 1984 Hall of Fame Bowl? How many completions? How many yards?

17. Who was the leading pass receiver in the 1984 Hall of Fame Bowl for Wisconsin? How many receptions? How many yards?

8
ROSE BOWLS

1. After tying what Big Ten opponent in 1952, Wisconsin was voted to represent the conference in the 1953 Rose Bowl?

2. In 1959 the Badgers rallied to beat what team to earn a second bid to the Rose Bowl?

3. What team defeated the Badgers in the 1953 Rose Bowl?

4. After only four seasons at Wisconsin, what Badger head coach took them to the 1994 Rose Bowl?

5. Who was the offensive line coach of the 1994 Rose Bowl Badgers?

6. Who scored the only Wisconsin touchdown of the 1960 Rose Bowl?

7. What future Green Bay Packer scored the only touchdown of the 1953 Rose Bowl?

8. What Big Ten team were the co-champions with the Badgers in the 1952 season?

9. What Badger All-American defensive end's career ended with a knee injury in the 1953 Rose Bowl game?

10. What was the final score of the 1953 Rose Bowl game?

11. Wisconsin's second trip to the Rose Bowl occurred in what year?

12. Who was the head coach of the Badgers second trip to Pasadena?

13. What team pulverized Wisconsin in the second Rose Bowl? What was the score?

14. Who was the Badgers quarterback in the second Rose Bowl?

15. The third trip to the Rose Bowl came in what year? Against what opponent?

16. Who was the record breaking Badger quarterback of the third Rose Bowl game?

17. How many records did this MVP Badger quarterback set in the third Wisconsin Rose Bowl?

18. Wisconsin had an outstanding receiver on the third Rose Bowl team. Who is he? How many pass receptions did he have that day? How many yards?

19. What was the final score of the third Rose Bowl game? Who was the Badgers' opponent?

20. The 80th Rose Bowl was Wisconsin's fourth Rose Bowl trip. Who did the Badgers play? What was the final score?

21. Who was voted the most valuable player of the 80th Rose Bowl game?

22. What were the statistics for the game's most valuable player?

23. Who was the Badgers' co-most valuable player of the third Rose Bowl game?

24. What was a huge play for the Badgers in the 80th Rose Bowl game?

25. Who were the two Badgers that were ejected from the 1994 Rose Bowl?

26. What team scored first in the 1994 Rose Bowl game? How were the points scored?

27. What wide receiver broke a Wisconsin record for pass receptions in the 1994 Rose Bowl game? How many receptions did he have?

28. Which 1994 team set a Rose Bowl record for fumbles lost in a game? How many?

29. Within 1,000, what was the attendance of the 80th Rose Bowl game?

30. What was the one incident that marred the Wisconsin Badgers appearance in the 1994 Rose Bowl game?

31. Wisconsin lost seven starters from the 1994 Rose Bowl team. Can you name three of them?

9
POSITIONS AND NUMBERS

Give the position and uniform number for the following players.

1. Al Toon
2. Tom Weisner
3. Rufus Ferguson
4. Tim Krumrie
5. Alan Ameche
6. Terrell Fletcher
7. Darrell Bevell
8. Yusef Burgess
9. Jeff Messenger
10. Brent Moss
11. Lee DeRamus
12. Mark Montgomery
13. Elroy Hirsch
14. Mike Webster
15. Billy Marek
16. Dave Schreiner
17. Pat Richter
18. Ron VanderKelen
19. Don Davey
20. Randy Wright
21. Ira Mathews
22. Troy Vincent

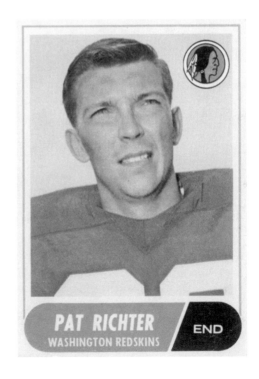

PAT RICHTER / END
WASHINGTON REDSKINS

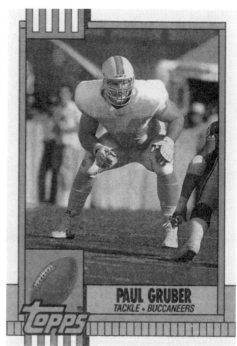

QUESTIONS

WISCONSIN BADGERS HOCKEY

1
INDIVIDUAL RECORDS

1. It took Jeff Larson just how long to score a goal at the beginning of the game against the University of Minnesota on October 30, 1982?

2. A hat trick is scoring three goals in a game by one individual. Who holds the record for career hat tricks for the Badgers?

3. Can you name the goalie that stopped a record 62 shots on goal, setting a Wisconsin record?

4. What Badger defenseman scored 19 times during the 1990-91 season?

5. What future 1980 Olympian had five assists and two goals against Denver on February 2, 1979?

6. He played 81 minutes and 28 seconds in goal against North Dakota on March 5, 1983. Who is he? Did the Badgers win the contest?

7. Three Badgers have scored 17 power play goals in a season. Can you name two of them? What seasons?

8. Who leads Wisconsin with 194 career assists?

9. What Badger scored four times in one period?

10. Two Badgers have scored in nine straight games. Can you name them?

11. Who holds the Badger record with 177 career penalities?

12. One Badger scored one or more points in 21 consecutive games. Who is he? What season?

13. What Badger holds the record for six short-handed goals in the 1972-73 season?

14. Only one Wisconsin hockey player has scored 90 points in a season. Who is he? What season?

15. Three Badgers have scored 100 or more goals in their Wisconsin hockey careers. Can you name two of them?

16. Who scored 10 game-winning goals in one season for Wisconsin?

17. During the 1988-89 season what Wisconsin goalie saved over 92% of the shots on goal?

18. What Badger scored two goals within 10 seconds of each other? Against what opponent?

19. What Wisconsin goalie holds the record for nine shutouts in a season?

20. This Badger scored the only three hat tricks during the 1971-72 season. Who is he?

21. This Badger scored a broken stick goal when the North Dakota goalie followed the broken piece of the stick and not the puck. This goal gave Wisconsin a 1-0 lead in the second game of the Western Collegiate Hockey Association playdown game on March 12, 1994. Who is he?

2
COACHES

1. The banner hanging from the overhead scoreboard in the Dane County Coliseum reads: "A Great Day For Hockey." Whose quote was this?

2. This head coach won two NCAA Championships with the Badgers. Who is he?

3. This head coach won three NCAA Championships with the Badgers. Who is he?

4. This coach served one season as the Badgers head coach, 1975-6. Who is he?

5. This assistant coach was with Wisconsin for 22 years. Who is he?

6. Who is the only Badger head coach with a losing career record?

7. This head coach has won 20 or more games in 12 consecutive seasons. Who is he?

8. Who are the three winningest head coaches in Badger hockey history through the 1993-94 seasons?

3
TEAM RECORDS

1. Wisconsin has defeated this team 14 straight times without a loss. What Eastern Association team is this?

2. What season did the Badgers win 37 and lost only 7 times?

3. What season did the Badgers win 19 of 20 home games?

4. Wisconsin lost the first nine games to this opponent, but entering the 1993-94 season has evened the career record at 34-34. What team did the Badgers catch?

5. In over 110 games played against this opponent, Wisconsin had beaten this team 75% of the time. What team is this?

6. How many seasons has Wisconsin won 20 or more games?

7. How many seasons has Wisconsin won 30 or more games?

8. How many times were the Badgers shutout between January 14, 1972 and December 27, 1979?

9. Wisconsin has led all of college hockey in average attendance for how many consecutive seasons?

10. How many seasons has Wisconsin won the WCHA playoffs?

11. Two seasons the Badgers ended as the runners-up in the NCAA playoffs. What seasons?

12. What Wisconsin opponent did the Badgers defeat 20-0 and 6-2 to open the 1981-82 season?

4
PERSONALITIES

1. Who was the Badger picked 11th overall in the National Hockey League draft? What year and what team selected him?

2. What Badgers played with five NHL teams in their professional careers?

3. Three Wisconsin players have been selected two times to the first team All-America college hockey team. Can you name two of them?

4. This Badger was drafted number 185 overall by the Calgary Flames, but made the team. Who is he and what year was he drafted?

5. Who were the two Badger goalies selected to the All-America first team? What years?

6. What Badger was named the most valuable player in the WCHA during the 1989-90 season?

7. Who was the goaltender awarded Wisconsin's most valuable player three straight seasons?

5
FIRSTS

1. What was the first season Wisconsin played in the Dane County Coliseum?

2. Where did the Badgers skate prior to moving to the Dane County Coliseum? What seasons?

3. What was the first team the Badgers defeated in 1963 after a 28 year absence of college hockey? Who scored the winning goal?

4. Who was the first Badger to score 100 goals in his career?

5. He was the first Wisconsin hockey player named to the All-WCHA first team. Who is he? What season?

6. Who was the first Badger goalie named to the All-WCHA first team? What season?

7. Who was the first All-American Wisconsin hockey player?

8. When was Wisconsin's first and only losing season at home?

9. He was the first and only Badger to have 10 game-winning goals. Who is he and what season?

10. This head coach first coached for 11 seasons at Colorado College before coming to Wisconsin. Who is he?

11. Who were Wisconsin's first co-coaches of hockey in the modern era after 28 years?

12. Wisconsin's first appearance in NCAA Final Four hockey

tournament was in what season?

13. Since 1948 the NCAA hockey finals have been played in Wisconsin for the first time in what year? What city?

14. Who was the first Badger ever to be drafted by the NHL? What season and what year?

15. What was Wisconsin's first season competing in the WCHA?

16. What was the Badgers first WCHA championship season?

6
OLYMPICS

1. The USA gold medal Olympic hockey team of 1980 played Wisconsin twice during their pre-Olympic schedule. Did the Badgers defeat the future gold medalists?

2. This Badger was the goalie for the 1984 Olympic team in Sarajevo, Yugoslavia. Who is he?

3. With one second remaining in the first period in the game against the USSR during the 1980 Olympics, this Badger grabbed the loose puck and scored to tie the game at two each. Who was this Badger?

4. What Wisconsin hockey player competed for Austria in the 1984 and 1988 Winter Olympics?

5. This Badger defenseman made the 1980 squad but played little during the Olympics at Lake Placid. Who is he?

6. What Badger competed in both the 1988 and 1992 Winter Olympics for the United States?

7. This Badger defenseman starred in the 1984 Winter Olympics and also went on to a successful NHL career. Who is he?

8. Name two of the three Wisconsin players on the USA hockey team in 1976 played at Innsbruck, Austria?

9. This Badger was a second team All-American defenseman in 1991 and played on the 1992 Olympic team at Albertville, France. Who is he?

10. What Badger was one of the goalies on the 1988 Olympic team in Calgary, Canada?

11. This University of Minnesota star opted to continue to play college hockey after winning the 1980 gold medal. He competed against the Badgers in the 1981 NCAA championship game. Who is he?

12. Between 1976-1988 the Badgers defeated the Olympic team only once. What year and what was significant about this victory?

13. Who was the lone Badger on the 1994 Olympic team?

14. This Wisconsin head coach was the Olympic head coach in the 1976 Winter Olympics. Can you name him?

7
NCAA CHAMPIONSHIPS

1973

1. What team did the Badgers defeat in the semi-final game in 1973, scoring with only five seconds left in regulation and winning in overtime?

2. What team did the Badgers defeat to win the 1973 NCAA tournament that was ranked number one nationally?

3. What Badger scored both game winning goals in the 1973 playoffs?

4. The 1973 hockey championship for Wisconsin was the university's first NCAA championship since 1956. What sport did Wisconsin win a championship in 1956?

1977

1. Both the semi-final and championship games in the 1977 NCAA hockey tournament went in to overtime. What team did Wisconsin beat in the semi-finals? In the championship game?

2. The 1976-77 Badgers finished with how many wins in 45 games played?

3. What Badger was named the most valuable player of the 1977 NCAA hockey tournament?

4. Two Badgers scored twice in the 1977 championship game. Can you name the two players?

1981

1. What was the significance of Wisconsin's 1981 championship?

2. What teams did Wisconsin defeat to win the 1981 title?

3. What Badger was named most valuable player of the 1981 tournament?

4. Two Badgers scored twice in the final game. Can you name them?

5. On the way to the NCAA crown, Wisconsin defeated the number one teams in the Eastern Collegiate Athletic Conference, Central Collegiate Hockey Association, and WCHA. Can you name the three teams?

1983

1. What was the only team to defeat the 1983 Badgers in their final 15 games?

2. What teams did Wisconsin defeat in the NCAA 1983 tournament?

3. Two Badgers scored twice in the 1983 championship game. Who were they?

4. What Badger was named most valubable player of the 1983 tournament?

1990

1. What teams did Wisconsin beat to win the 1990 NCAA championship?

2. What Badger was named the 1990 tournament most valuable

player?

3. What Wisconsin player scored a hat trick in the championship game?

4. Who was the Wisconsin goalie in the 1990 title game?

THE
ANSWERS

WISCONSIN BADGERS BASKETBALL

1
INDIVIDUAL RECORDS

1. Ken Barnes. He also had 23 rebounds that game.
2. Danny Jones, (1986-90) 1,854 points.
3. Rick Olson.
4. Claude "Stretch" Gregory.
5. Clarence Sherrod.
6. Michael Finley.
7. 35 straight free throws.
8. Brad Sellers.
9. Jim Clinton.
10. Joe Franklin 11.9 rebounds (1966-68), Kim Hughes 11.2 rebounds (1972-74), Jack Brens 10.4 rebounds (1962-64).
11. Tracy Webster.
12. Terry Dischinger.
13. Quinn Buckner.
14. Marty Gharrity.
15. Lew Alcindor (Kareem Abdul-Jabbar).
16. Larry Petty.
17. Walter Hirschberg (1899, 1900, 1901).
18. Patrick Tompkins.
19. Brian Good 57-63, .905, 1990.
20. Ken Morrow.
21. Claude Gregory (1978-81), Danny Jones (1987-90), Clarence Sherrod (1969-71).
22. Rick Olson (1983-86) 112, Danny Jones (1987-90) 109, Joe Chrnelich (1977-80) 108.
23. Tim Locum.

24. Danny Jones 611 points, Trent Jackson 574 points.
25. Michael Finley.
26. Clarence Sherrod, 1970.

2
TEAM RECORDS

1. 1947.
2. 1930.
3. Minnesota Golden Gophers beginning in 1900.
4. Northwestern.
5. Southern Methodist, 120-82.
6. 1954, 107-68 against Louisiana State.
7. Washington State, 39-34.
8. "Badgers Bring Home Bacon"
9. Joe Franklin 11.8, Ken Barnes 11.1, Mark Zubor 11.2, Mike Carlin 10.3, Ken Gustafson 13.8.
10. 1946-47.
11. 1980.
12. Three overtime periods.
13. Four.
14. University of Denver. Biggest win ever by Wisconsin. 89-34.
15. University of Chicago, 10 points.
16. 24 games which lasted from Dec. 13, 1913 to another loss to the University of Chicago on January 23, 1915. The Badgers won 53 of 54 games during the streak.
17. 14 times.
18. Minnesota Golden Gophers. 10th largest loss margin in Badger history.
19. Jerry Lucas, Larry Siegfried, John Havlicek, Joe Roberts, Mel Noel.
20. Four times, 1962, 1963, 1966, 1967.
21. Bill Cofield coached Wisconsin. Al McGuire coached Marquette. The

Badgers lost both games.
22. 19 years. First time since 1974.
23. 1946-47 Michigan, 58-57; 1958-59 Purdue 91-86.
24. 14 games in a row.
25. Purdue, February 1, 1976.
26. 37. Yes, 74-52.
27. 1899.
28. UCLA December 28, 1966 (100-56) 44-point loss. November 25, 1972 (94-53) 41-point loss.
29. Defeated New Orleans, 63-61, lost to St. Louis, 73-68.
30. University of Cincinnati. Yes, 80-72.

3
PERSONALITIES

1. Kim and Kerry Hughes.
2. John Powless.
3. Michael Finley.
4. Ken Siebel. 1961, 1962, 1963.
5. Lamont Weaver.
6. Rashard Griffith.
7. Eino Hendrickson (1967, 1968, 1970), Bob Hinga (1973), Grant Johnson (1991, 1992, 1993).
8. Larry Hisle, Jr. 1990-91.
9. Don Rehfeldt 1950, center, averaged 19.8 points a game. Rehfeldt was drafted by Baltimore in the first round - second overall. Also was Big Ten most valuable player.
10. Chuck Nagle.
11. Dale Hackbart.
12. Pat Richter.

4
NATIONAL BASKETBALL ASSOCIATION

1. Joe Franklin 1968, John Schell 1969, J.J.Weber 1987.
2. Albert Henry by Philadelphia in 1970, Wes Matthews by Washington in 1980.
3. New York Knicks 1989-91.
4. Gene Englund.

5
COACHES

1. Ken Anderson.
2. Walter Meanwell 1912 and 1916.
3. Harold Foster.
4. John Erickson.
5. Steve Yoder.
6. Milt Bruhn.
7. Harold Foster.
8. Walter Meanwell.
9. Bill Cofield, 1981-82 season. 21 losses.
10. 1940-41 season, Harold Foster.
11. James Elsom.

6
FIRSTS

1. Gene Englund, 1941.
2. Wes Matthews, 106 in 1979.
3. Don Rehfeldt 1944-50.
4. Joe Franklin, 1968. 202 Field goals.
5. Intercollegiate Conference of Faculty Representatives.
6. Dick Cable.

7
WHAT NUMBER
DID THEY WEAR?

1. 35.
2. 11.
3. 12.
4. 23.
5. 32.
6. 32.
7. 35.
8. 44.
9. 44.
10. 24.
11. 50.
12. 25.
13. 11.
14. 23.
15. 45.

8
WHAT POSITION DID THEY PLAY?

1. Forward.
2. Guard.
3. Guard.
4. Guard.
5. Center.
6. Forward.
7. Forward.
8. Center.
9. Forward.
10. Guard.
11. Center.
12. Forward.
13. Guard.
14. Guard.
15. Forward.
16. Center.

WISCONSIN BADGERS
FOOTBALL

1
TEAM RECORDS

1. 1896.
2. 1889.
3. Minnesota Golden Gophers. 1890.
4. 1901.
5. 10 wins, 1 loss, 1 tie.
6. Seven; three by Terrell Fletcher, two by Brent Moss, one by Mark Montgomery, one by Carl McCullough.
7. 1991 against Northwestern Wildcats.
8. 1989 against Illinois Illini.
9. 1985 against Northern Illinois Huskies.
10. 1992 against Bowling Green.
11. 1991 against Purdue Boilermakers.
12. October 7, 1952 after a 20-6 victory over Illinois.
13. 1942 Ohio State Buckeyes, 1962 Northwestern Wildcats, 1981 Michigan Wolverines.
14. 10 against New Mexio State.
15. Four. Against Minnesota 1976, Kentucky 1984, Bowling Green 1992, Purdue 1992.
16. 13 against Miami (FL) in 1989.
17. 17, 1900-1902, stopped by Michigan.
18. 25, 1900-1903, stopped by University of Chicago.
19. 1897 (9-1-0), 1898 (9-1-0), 1899 (9-2-0), 1901 (9-0-0), 1993 (9-1-1).
20. 1901 (9-0-0), 1906 (5-0-0), 1912 (7-0-0).
21. Nine: 1898, 1897, 1901, 1906, 1912, 1952, 1959, 1962, 1993.
22. Whitewater, 1890.

23. 1889 (0-2), 1967 (0-9-1), 1968 (0-10).
24. 1896, 1897, 1901(tied), 1906, 1912, 1952, 1959, 1962, 1993(tied).
25. Four. 1956 (0-4-3), 1967 (0-6-1), 1968 (0-7-0), 1990 (0-8-0).
26. 43-38-5.

2
CAMP RANDALL STADIUM

1. 77,745.
2. November 3, 1917.
3. Minnesota, 10-7.
4. "Fifth Quarter".
5. Michael Leckrone.
6. Billy Marek, five touchdowns.
7. 66,557.
8. Troy Vincent, 90 yards.
9. Todd Gregoire, 54 yards.
10. Billy Lowe, 98 yards.
11. Tom Brigham, 91 yards.
12. Ira Matthews and Michael Jones, 100 yards.
13. Tony Lowery to Lee DeRamus, 89 yards.

3
PERSONALITIES

1. Alan "The Horse" Ameche.
2. Don Davey.
3. Randy Wright.
4. 35 - Alan Ameche, 40 - Elroy "Crazy Legs" Hirsch, 80 - Dave Schreiner, 83 - Allan Shafer.
5. Al Toon, Paul Gruber, Troy Vincent.
6. Jeff Dellenbach, Don Davey, Rick Graf, Paul Gruber, Richard Johnson, Tim Krumrie, Nate Odemes, Michael Reid, Al Toon, Dan Turk, Troy Vincent.
7. Pat O'Dea, Robert Butler, Marty Below, Pat Harder, Dave Schreiner, Elroy Hirsch, Alan Ameche.
8. Bob Wilson.
9. Chuck Belin. Los Angeles Rams.
10. Don Davey.
11. Troy Vincent.
12. Chuck Belin, offensive lineman; Barry Alvarez, coach.
13. Center Ken Bowman.
14. Pat Richter, Ron VanderKelen.
15. Al Toon, New York Jets; Richard Johnson, Houston Oilers; Darryl Sims, Pittsburgh Steelers.
16. Pat Richter.
17. Buckingham U. Badger or "Bucky" for short.

4
INDIVIDUAL RECORDS

1. Alan Ameche, Brent Moss, Larry Emery, Rufus Ferguson, Billy Marek.
2. Dick Milaeger, 52.2 yards average.
3. Earl Girard against Iowa, November 8, 1947.
4. Bill Lane, 10 against Indiana Hoosiers, November 3, 1951.
5. Lee DeRamus, 89 yard touchdown.
6. George O'Brian, 96 yards.
7. Darrell Bevell, Randy Wright, 19 touchdown passes.
8. Clarence Bratl, four against Minnesota, November 20, 1954.
9. Dave Crossen, 18.
10. Bob Radcliffe, against Navy October

15, 1949.

11. Michael Reid, three against Ohio State.

12. Richard Johnson, against Missouri, September 15, 1984.

13. Rich Thompson, 22.

14. Ira Matthews.

15. Richard Johnson, six, 1984.

16. Randy Wright, 330 attempts.

17. Mike Howard, 182 completions.

18. Lee DeRamus setting the record of 920 in the 1993 season.

19. Al Toon, Lee DeRamus, 54 receptions.

20. Al Toon, 9 touchdowns.

21. Billy Marek, 18 touchdowns.

22. Brent Moss, 276 attempts.

23. Kevin Rohde.

24. Dave Fronek, 72 punts.

25. Thad McFadden.

26. Fred Owens, 30 returns.

27. Nate Odomes, 616 yards.

28. Neovia Greyer.

29. David Greenwood, 156 yards.

30. Michael Reid.

31. Dave Lokanc, 181 tackles.

32. Don Davey, Darryl Sims, 24 tackles.

33. Don Davey, 117 tackles.

34. Brent Moss and Terrell Fletcher, 2,411 yards.

5
THE 1993 SEASON

1. Darrell Bevell, 5 touchdown passes.

2. 423 yards completing 31 of 48 passes.

3. John Coatta.

4. Mike Thompson.

5. Jeff Messenger.

6. Yusef Burgess.

7. Brent Moss.

8. Michigan Wolverines, 13-10.

9. Minnesota Golden Gophers, 28-21.

10. Rich Schnetzky.

11. December 4, 1993 at Tokyo, Japan. Michigan State Spartans.

12. Ninth.

13. Brent Moss, 1479 yards.

6
COACHES

1. Phil King.

2. Harry Stuhldreher, 13 years.

3. Ivy Williamson.

4. Milt Bruhn.

5. Dave McClain, 11.

6. Phil King, 65-11-1, .851 winning percentage.

7
THE LESSER BOWLS

1. Tennessee Volunteers, 28-21.

2. Kansas State, 14-3.

3. Kentucky Wildcats, 20-19.

4. Chucky Davis, 44 yards.

5. Randy Wright, 123 yards with 9 completions.

6. Jeffrey Nault, 85 yards with 5 catches.

7. 53, 220.

8. John Williams, 57 yards.

9. Randy Wright, 183 yards with 9 completions.

10. David Keeling, 4 receptions for 64 yards.

11. Randy Wright, Tim Krumrie.

12. Randy Wright.
13. 23 mile per hour wind dropping temperature wind chill to -10 degrees. Game was played at Shreveport, Louisania.
14. A fumbled snap on a 26-yard game winning field goal attempt.
15. Joseph Armentrout, 105 yards.
16. Mike Howard, 19 completions for 203 yards.
17. Bret Pearson, 5 receptions for 55 yards.

8
ROSE BOWLS

1. Purdue Boilermakers.
2. Minnesota Golden Gophers.
3. University of Southern California.
4. Barry Alvarez.
5. Billy Callahan.
6. Tom Wiesner.
7. Al Carmichael.
8. Purdue.
9. Don Voss.
10. 7-0, USC over Wisconsin.
11. 1960.
12. Milt Bruhn.
13. Washington Huskies, 44-8.
14. Dale Hackbart.
15. Southern California, 1963.
16. Ron VanderKelen.
17. Four: Pass attempts, completions, yards, total offense.
18. Pat Richter, 11 receptions for 163 yards.
19. USC 42, Wisconsin 37.
20. UCLA, Wisconsin 21, UCLA 16.
21. Brent Moss.
22. 158 yards in 36 attempts with two touchdowns.
23. Ron VanderKelen.
24. Darrell Bevell's 21-yard touchdown run.
25. Fullback Mark Montgomery and receiver Lee DeRamus.
26. UCLA, Field goal.
27. J.J. Stokes (UCLA) 14 receptions.
28. UCLA, five fumbles-five lost.
29. 101,237.
30. The ticket mess where over 2,000 Badger fans watched the game from a nearby tent.
31. Joe Panos, Mark Montgomery on offense. Lamark Shackerford, Carlos Fowler, Yusef Burgess, Reggie Holt, Scott Nelson on defense.

9
WHAT POSITION DID THEY PLAY? WHAT NUMBER DID THEY WEAR?

1. Wide receiver, 87.
2. Fullback, 38.
3. Tailback, 21.
4. Nose Guard, 50.
5. Fullback, 35.
6. Running back, 41.
7. Quarterback, 11.
8. Linebacker, 98.
9. Cornerback, 29.
10. Running back, 33.
11. Wide receiver, 2.
12. Running back, 32.
13. Running back, 40.
14. Center, 51.
15. Running back, 26.
16. Wide receiver, 80.
17. Receiver, punter, 88.
18. Quarterback, 15.

19. Defensive end/tackle, 91.
20. Quarterback, 12.
21. Kickoff/punt returns, 25.
22. Defensive back, 22.

WISCONSIN BADGERS HOCKEY

1
INDIVIDUAL RECORDS

1. Seven seconds.
2. Bert DeHate, 1967-69.
3. Jim Makey, Michigan State a 4-3 victory.
4. Sean Hill.
5. Bob Suter.
6. Marc Behrend. Yes, 6-5 in three overtimes.
7. Chris Tancill 1989-90, Peter Johnson 1980-81, Mark Johnson 1976-77.
8. Theran Welch 1977-81.
9. Mark Fitzgerald, February 24, 1967, against Ohio University in the second period.
10. Steve Alley 1976, John Byce 1990.
11. Bob Suter 1975-79.
12. Mike Eaves, November 1977 thru February 1978.
13. Norm Cherrey.
14. Mark Johnson 1978-79.
15. Mark Johnson 125, Bert DeHate 108, Tony Granato 100 goals.
16. John Newberry 1981-82.
17. Curtis Joseph.
18. Steve Alley against Michigan State on January 29, 1977.
19. Terry Kleisinger 1980-84.
20. Gary Winchester.

21. Mickey Elick.

2
COACHES

1. Bob Johnson.
2. Jeff Sauer.
3. Bob Johnson.
4. Bill Rothwell.
5. Bill Howard, goalie coach.
6. Bill Rothwell, 1975-76 season with a 12-24 record.
7. Jeff Sauer.
8. John Riley 34 victories, Jeff Sauer 297 victories through the 1992-93 season, Bob Johnson 367 victories.

3
TEAM RECORDS

1. New Hampshire.
2. 1976-77.
3. 1972-73.
4. Michigan State Spartans.
5. Colorado College. 87-27-3 entering the 1993-94 season.
6. 24 seasons.
7. Five seasons. 1976-77, 1981-82, 1982-83, 1987-88, 1989-90.
8. None.
9. 25, 1970 to the present.
10. Nine times.
11. 1983 North Dakota, 1992 Lake Superior State.
12. Windsor.

4
PERSONALITIES

1. Mike Blaisdell in 1980 by the Detroit Red Wings.
2. Mark Johnson and Brian Engblom.
3. Mike Eaves 1977-78, Mark Johnson 1978-79, Craig Norwich 1976-77.
4. Gary Suter 1984.
5. Julian Baretta 1977, Roy Schultz 1980.
6. Gary Shuchuk.
7. Gary Johnson 1964-67.

5
FIRSTS

1. 1967.
2. Hartmeyer Arena 1963-67.
3. Macalester, Chan Young.
4. Bert DeHate. 1966-70, 108 goals.
5. Brian Engblom, 1974-75.
6. Julian Baretta, 1976-77.
7. John Jagger.
8. 1975-76. 6 wins, 12 losses.
9. John Newberry, 1981-82.
10. Jeff Sauer.
11. Art Thomsen and John Riley.
12. 1969-70.
13. 1993, Milwaukee.
14. Norm Cherrey. 1971, Vancouver Canucks.
15. 1970-71.
16. 1976-77.

6
OLYMPICS

1. No, Wisconsin lost both games. January 15, 1980 6-2 and January 22, 1980 4-2.
2. Marc Behrend.
3. Mark Johnson.
4. Ed Lebler.
5. Bob Suter.
6. Jim Johannson.
7. Chris Chelios.
8. Steve Alley, Bob Lundeen and John Taft.
9. Sean Hill.
10. Mike Richter.
11. Neal Broten.
12. January 7, 1984. Wisconsin was the only American college team to beat the Olympic team on the pre-Olympic schedule.
13. Barry Richter.
14. Bob Johnson.

7
NCAA CHAMPIONSHIPS

1973

1. Cornell.
2. University of Denver, 4-2.
3. Dean Talafous.
4. Boxing.

1977
1. New Hampshire, Michigan.
2. 37 wins.
3. Goalie Julian Baretta.
4. Mark Johnson and Steve Alley both scored twice.

1981

1. After losing a total goal series to Colorado College 13-12, the Badgers were given an at-large berth bid to the NCAA tournament and won the championship.
2. Northern Michigan in the semi-finals, 5-1. Minnesota in the championship game 6-3.
3. Marc Behrend.
4. John Newberry and Ed Lebler each scored twice.
5. Clarkson, Northern Michigan, Minnesota

1983

1. Minnesota, 5-1, February 19, 1983.
2. Providence in the semi-finals, 2-0. Harvard, 5-2, in the championship game.
3. Pat Flatley and Paul Houston each scored twice.
4. Marc Behrend, goalie. Second time in three years.

1990

1. Boston College, 2-1, in the semi-finals. Colgate, 7-3, in the championship game.
2. Chris Tancill.
3. John Byce.
4. Duane Derksen.

RANDY WRIGHT
QB • Packers

PRO SET • THE OFFICIAL NFL CARD

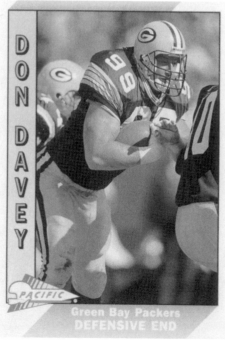

DON DAVEY

PACIFIC

Green Bay Packers
DEFENSIVE END

ABOUT THE AUTHORS

LINDA

- Graduated from New London, Wisconsin High School in 1975.
- A devoted Badger fan since she was ten years old - primarily football.
- Carries a 168 average in bowling.
- Co-coaches basketball with Jeff.
- Avid landscaper.
- Does community service throughout the year in Clintonville, Wisconsin.
- Bookkeeper/manager of Everson's IGA in Clintonville.

JEFF

- Graduated from Clintonville, Wisconsin High School in 1969.
- Graduated from the University of Wisconsin system in 1973.
- Author of *A Civic Century: Clintonville's New Generation 1955-1986*.
- Author of *This Date in Milwaukee Brewers History 1970-1987*.
- Author of *Milwaukee Brewers - Facts & Trivia.*
- Coached fifth and sixth grade basketball since 1978.
- Avid curler.
- Owner/operator of Everson's IGA in Clintonville.
- Married Linda in 1992.
- Raises their children Katie, Kyle and Alexandra with Linda.